INTERNATIONAL BANK FOR RECONS  DEVELOPMENT

DATE DUE

WORLD BANK STAFF OCCASIONAL PAPERS NUMBER ONE

HERMAN G. VAN DER TAK

THE ECONOMIC CHOICE BETWEEN HYDROELECTRIC AND THERMAL POWER DEVELOPMENTS

with a Note on Joint Costs in Multipurpose Projects

Distributed by The Johns Hopkins Press

LC66002853
6002089987

w

FOREWORD

The benefits of research are greater the further they are spread. Some of the work done within or for the Bank and its affiliated organizations may be useful to others who are engaged in the practice of sound economic development. Accordingly, we have decided to publish papers based on this work from time to time, and this volume is the first of such publications. Most of the papers likely to be published will have an unashamed pragmatic bias, as indeed has the work of the development economist generally. Because these papers are published by the Bank, however, it by no means follows that their premises or conclusions are accepted by the Bank either in practice or theory; they are the responsibility of the authors. We hope the papers may be a modest stimulus to further research, particularly in the troubled zone where theory meets real life.

September 23, 1966

George D. Woods
President
International Bank for Reconstruction and Development

TABLE OF CONTENTS

Tables

Charts

PREFACE

Essential to the proper planning of development in a country is the allocation of scarce resources to its best advantage. The scarcer these resources are, the more important it is not to waste them. This paper deals with one of the most commonly experienced problems of choice in a developing country, when the decision is whether to make a large investment in hydro power now or a series of smaller investments in thermal power later.

The author is grateful for criticism by past and present colleagues in the group working on problems of resource allocation, both in the Economics Department and in the Projects Department, and in particular to Kenneth E. Bohr. Benjamin B. King has greatly contributed to the exposition of the Note on Joint Costs. The views expressed in this paper and in others are in no way to be taken as representing the views of the Bank. The authors alone are responsible for their approach and accuracy.

This staff study is part of continuing work in the Economics Department on problems of resource allocation. While we expect that most of the occasional papers will originate from this and other work in the Economics Department, we also hope to publish work from other parts of the Bank group, including technical papers that have a bearing on economic analysis.

Hugh Latimer is the editor of the series and the Editorial Committee, in addition, is composed of:

Barend A. de Vries, Chairman   Samuel Lipkowitz
John H. Adler   H. O. Schmitt
Bernard Bell   R. M. Sundrum
Patrick de Fontenay   C. H. Thompson

September 23, 1966

Andrew M. Kamarck
Director
Economics Department

INTERNATIONAL BANK FOR RECONSTRUCTION AND DEVELOPMENT

WORLD BANK STAFF OCCASIONAL PAPERS NUMBER ONE

I

INTRODUCTION

1.   The essence of the economic evaluation process is determining whether a project involves a better use of resources than its possible alternatives. The evaluation of the costs and benefits may differ depending on the purpose of the evaluation. From the point of view of national resource use, the evaluation should be in terms of real (social) costs and benefits. In many cases the alternatives themselves may not be clear and the comparison cannot be specific but relates to a hypothetical marginal project which might be undertaken in lieu of the project under evaluation. This is the purpose of using what is known as the "opportunity cost of capital," a minimum rate of return to represent what capital might earn in alternative marginal uses. If a project is expected to yield less than this minimum, it should not be undertaken, for there are presumably more productive uses for capital elsewhere. Cases where specific alternatives are under consideration representing different ways of producing the same good or service whose need is given belong to a special type of this general problem. The immediate comparison is then clear. The choice is limited to the given alternatives, one of which must be selected. The opportunity cost of capital comes into

3

the problem in helping to determine which of the alternatives involves the most economical use of resources in the light of general investment opportunities in the economy.

2. An excellent example of this special type is the comparison of alternative methods of producing electric power. The power benefits are the same; the only question is which method of supply is the cheapest. A kilowatt-hour is a kilowatt-hour, whatever way it is produced. This is an important problem in practice since it is at the basis of the economic appraisal of all hydroelectric projects. In some cases the answer is obvious. The cost of fuel may be very high and the cost of constructing hydro plants very low. In others, however, more detailed analysis of the alternatives may be essential to the appraisal and although the problem of determining the least expensive solution may be simple in concept, the analysis itself may not be so.

3. It is the purpose of this paper to set down in a systematic way a logically correct method for handling the economic comparison of alternative power developments. The discounted cash flow method of computing returns which is used here has come to be generally accepted in recent years. There is no need to give a detailed justification of this approach at this date; that has already been done most competently by others.[1] However, there is merit in working out an example of a specific and important application. By focussing on the technique itself and pointing out ways in which the analysis may be simplified, this paper may be of particular use to others faced with similar appraisal problems. It should go without saying that the less an appraisal team has to concern itself with problems of method, the more it can concentrate on the essential aspects of its analysis.

4. Furthermore, if the method is well understood and if some preliminary appraisal has already been made by consultants, the

---

[1] See, for example, "Project Evaluation, The Return on Capital," B. B. King, *Investment Criteria and Project Appraisal*, EDI/IBRD, Washington, D.C. 1961; *Principles of Engineering Economy*, E. L. Grant and W. G. Ireson, N.Y. 1960; *Water Supply, Economics, Technology and Policy*, J. Hirshleifer, J. C. DeHaven and J. W. Milliman, Chicago 1960. (See especially Chapter VII.)

sensitivity of the results to changes in key data can be worked out in advance so that effort in the field may be concentrated on the most critical items. If lack of provisional data prevents this, the same procedure can be applied to the team's own preliminary results, so that critical variables may be pinpointed at this stage and subjected to further scrutiny. In any case analysis is required to determine under what conditions, if any, the project is justified. This is particularly important if estimates of future developments depend on decisions which have still to be made and which could materially affect the attractiveness of a project.

5. This paper deals with the problem of comparing alternative developments of a power system to supply a projected demand for power, with specific load characteristics that must be met.[2] It is essentially a comparison of a hydro with a thermal system. However, the method employed need not necessarily be confined to comparisons of power projects. Any possible set of alternatives can be compared and, in fact, the method can equally well be applied to any number of alternatives.

6. To make the demonstration realistic the data used in this paper are in large part based on the preliminary work sheets of an actual project. (See Appendix A).

---

[2] In the case considered here, it is assumed that there are no irrigation, navigation or flood control benefits associated with the hydro project. Where there are such benefits, the problem of analysis is more complicated since the investment cost of the hydro power cannot be determined simply. See Appendix B.

II

COMPARISON OF HYDRO AND THERMAL POWER ALTERNATIVES: GENERAL SHAPE OF THE PROBLEM

7. The task is to compare alternative ways to produce electricity to meet the *same expected demand*,[3] and the economic selection problem is simply to determine which way is the cheapest. It is assumed that the expected demand for power must be met. The question is not whether to invest in power or in some other sector but rather which *type* of power investment represents the best use of resources given the decision to invest in power. In other words, benefits from the investment, however measured, are the same regardless of which system of development is chosen. Only the costs are different.

8. Note that this is not simply a question of comparing generating and transmission costs of hydro and thermal plants. The choice of hydro or thermal project will affect differently the operation, and cost, of the whole power system. The path of expansion of capacity will differ in each alternative. The hydro development will almost

---

[3] Techniques of estimating future demands for power, and of designing corresponding system developments, are not discussed here. This paper is concerned only with the analysis of the cost data thus obtained—by far the simpler task.

certainly include some thermal plants, and the thermal alternative may include hydroelectric plants. The correct cost comparison relates therefore to alternative system developments rather than to alternative hydro or thermal plants.

9. The comparison of costs between the two alternatives is not straightforward, as the alternatives have decidedly different patterns of expenditures over time. Typically the hydro alternative will involve higher expenditures in the early years and the thermal alternative higher expenditures in the later years. In a simplified way, the choice can be stated in terms of whether higher investment costs of hydro in the early years are or are not justified by its lower operating costs in the later years.[4] The only way a proper comparison can be made between series of expenditures with different time patterns (cash flows) is by making specific allowance for the time factor and summing them up as of a particular point in time. This is accomplished by discounting the two cash flows to a common year. The sum of the discounted values, that is the "present values," can then be compared directly. This procedure involves three types of decision—what is to be included in the costs or expenditures, over what length of time should the computations be extended, and what interest rate should be used for discounting.

10. In the calculation of costs, only actual expenditures on goods and services should be included and these should be entered in the year in which they occur. Financial charges and accounting items, such as interest, depreciation and amortization, should be excluded. Depreciation and interest on capital investment are taken into account by the discounting procedure itself. Amortization and interest on loans are financial items dependent on specific terms of financing and not inherent in the nature of the project. They are not relevant for the economic appraisal.[5]

---

[4] This is illustrated in Chart 1 for a complicated and realistic case. See paragraph 15.

[5] If, in a particular case, foreign financing is available at subsidized rates for one project and would not otherwise become available, this should of course be taken into account.

CHART 1

COMPARISON OF (UNDISCOUNTED) CASH FLOWS OF HYDRO AND THERMAL DEVELOPMENTS— LOWER LOAD

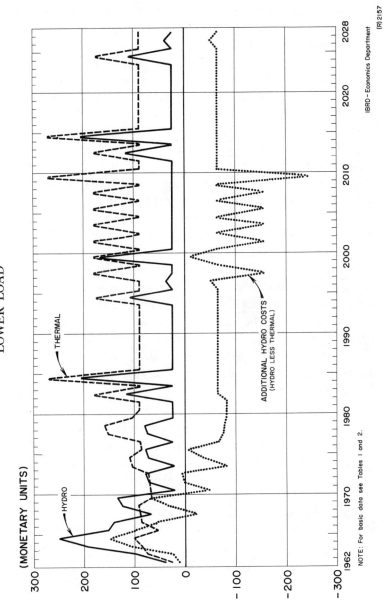

(MONETARY UNITS)

THERMAL

HYDRO

ADDITIONAL HYDRO COSTS (HYDRO LESS THERMAL)

300

200

100

0

-100

-200

-300

1962   1970   1980   1990   2000   2010   2020   2028

NOTE: For basic data see Tables I and 2.

IBRD – Economics Department

(R) 2157

9

11.   The length of time over which the cash flow should be extended depends on circumstances, and falls into two parts. The first period covers the years of *expansion* of the system. It continues until the year whereafter the relative costs of alternative ways of further expanding the system are no longer significantly prejudiced by the investment decision now taken. This period defines the alternative system developments to be compared. Often it will end in the year of full utilization of the power capacity of a hydro dam. For the purpose of calculating the return on additional hydro investment, expansion of the system stops in that year.[6] The cash flows, however, should be further extended for a second period which extends until *differences* in costs of operating the alternative systems at the *constant* level reached become insignificant in terms of their discounted present worth.[7] These costs involve not only expenses for full maintenance and current operation, but also for replacement investments, the latter being entered in the year in which they fall due. This applies to necessary replacement both of existing plant and of new plant installed during the expansion period. Replacement does not necessarily consist of exactly the same units as previously installed. It may be more reasonable to replace them by units of a larger size, more appropriate to the level of output reached in the meanwhile. For thermal plant, lifetime is usually taken to be 30 years and for hydro plant 60 years. Life of dam and reservoir may be longer still.

12.   Finally, these flows of costs should be compared. The same answer may be obtained by different methods. One method is to find, by trial and error, the rate of discount which equalizes the present worth of the two cost streams to be compared. Alterna-

---

[6] This is not necessarily so. Building the dam may make possible a later second stage of the project—or construction of a dam elsewhere in the same river system, providing cheaper additional power than from alternative thermal plants. As long as the present investment decision significantly influences such later investment choices, the expansion of the system should be extended for the purpose of appraisal.

[7] It might be asked why the period of comparison should not be extended to the lifetime of the project. But what is the lifetime of the project? That of the dam, the equipment, or the system as a whole? Luckily, at any discount rate used in practice the differences in operating costs of the two systems will become negligible before this point becomes an issue.

tively, the same result may be obtained by deducting the thermal cost stream from the hydro cost stream, thus obtaining one stream of positive and negative items, as shown by the dotted line in Chart 1. The positive items are the additional costs of the hydro alternative, and occur mainly in the earlier years; the negative items are the savings in cost of the hydro alternative (its benefits). The discount rate which equalizes the present worth of the positive and of the negative items will be the same as the one which equalizes the present value of the two separate cost streams and may be thought of as the rate of return on the additional (initial) investment in the hydro alternative.

13.   The rate of return thus obtained should be compared with the estimated opportunity cost of capital (the so-called shadow rate of interest) in order to assess whether the return is adequate. Alternatively, this same rate (opportunity cost of capital) may be used to obtain the present worth of the cost streams of the two alternatives. The alternative with the lowest cost, in terms of present worth, should be considered the better project.

III

IMPACT OF VARIATIONS IN COSTS AND PRICES ON THE RETURN ON THE ADDITIONAL HYDRO INVESTMENT

14. The foregoing exposition has been concerned only with the form of the calculations. It assumes that all the necessary data on costs and markets are given. In actual appraisals, however, the available data are often incomplete and always of varying quality. For some items, reliable cost estimates may be relatively easy to obtain; for others, data may simply not exist. In some cases, it may be possible to relate the projections of demand to firmly-based future trends in its main determinants; in others, this may not be so, especially if the future demand is expected to be heavily dependent on particular investments in power intensive industries, which may or may not take place at a given time. Furthermore, the cost of foreign exchange may be undervalued and the cost of labor overvalued in terms of their real cost to the economy. Thus the appraisal must be made on the basis of data with widely differing degrees of reliability. It is necessary to appraise the data, improve them where possible, organize them so as to give an answer within the limits of their accuracy, and so come up with a judgment on the overall economic merits of the project. It is thus obviously important to be able to determine the effect on the overall outcome of variations in the main cost and demand parameters of the problem; only then

can efforts of estimation, and necessary judgments, be focussed on the most critical elements of the appraisal. Section III will consider ways of estimating the impact of variations in costs. The influence of different demand patterns will be taken up in Section IV.

15. Henceforward to paragraph 30 inclusive, the data are taken from developments of an actual case. (See also Appendix A.) Tables 1 and 2 show detailed undiscounted cash flows for the hydro development and the thermal development[8] respectively, both to meet the *"lower load."*[9] The column headed "total" in each table reappears as a single line in Chart 1, with a third line showing the difference between them. Only these totals are required for calculating the return on the higher initial investment in the hydro development. It will be seen that, when discounted at $7\frac{1}{2}\%$, the present worths of the cash cost streams of both hydro and thermal developments are about 1260 monetary units. This indicates that, at the lower load forecast, the return on the additional hydro investment is $7\frac{1}{2}\%$.

The Use of Sub-Cashflows for Cost Components

16. The purpose of breaking down the cashflows by components, as shown in Tables 1 and 2, is to test the extent to which this outcome is altered if some of the cost items are different. The degree of disaggregation, and the categories of cost selected, depend upon the particular case to be investigated, but as a minimum such items as dam, hydro units, thermal plant and fuel costs should be specified. The various sub-cashflows, for each of the cost components, are then each discounted at $7\frac{1}{2}\%$. The results are shown at the bottom of Tables 1 and 2, and summarized in Table 3. The present worth has been calculated separately for costs occurring in the period 1962-1980 (the expansion period), and 1981-2028 (the constant period). Thus

---

[8] Hydro development and thermal development refer to alternative *system* developments; the hydro alternative does, in fact, include some use of thermal plants, as may be seen from Table 1.

[9] A more rapid growth of demand for power—the "higher" load—is discussed in Section IV below; cf. Tables 4 and 5.

TABLE 1: Cash Flow of Costs — Hydro Development — Lower Load

(monetary units)

Year	Investment						Operating expenses				Total
	Dam	Hydro units	Transmission 400 kv	Transmission 230 kv	Transmission 115 kv	Thermal plant	Production plant[a]	Fuel	Transmission	Frequency conversion	
Undiscounted											
1962	11,750				2,000		16,440	9,959			38,149
1963	23,600			14,000	2,000		16,440	11,086		30,000	97,126
1964	106,200			25,000	2,000		16,440	11,763		30,000	191,403
1965	147,500			36,000			16,440	13,695		30,000	247,635
1966	74,900	51,100		12,900			14,620	9,296	830		150,746
1967	43,300	57,200					14,620	10,704	830		139,554
1968			38,700				14,620	13,624	959		67,903
1969		51,100	51,500				16,220	3,532	959		123,311
1970		57,200	52,300				16,220	7,540	959		134,219
1971							16,520	2,052	2,384		20,956
1972		51,100					16,520	2,052	2,384		72,056
1973		57,200					16,520	2,052	2,384		78,156
1974		—					17,520	2,052	2,384		21,956
1975		51,100					17,520	2,052	2,384		73,056
1976		57,200					17,520	2,052	2,384		79,156
1977		—					18,620	2,052	2,384		23,056
1978		51,100					18,620	2,052	2,384		74,156
1979		57,200					18,620	2,052	2,384		80,256
1980		—					19,320	2,052	2,384		23,756

14

Year											
... (1981)						19,320	2,052	2,384	23,756		
1983			90,000			↑	↑	↑	↑		+90,000
...											
1985			180,000								+180,000
...											
1995				77,000	6,000						+83,000
1997				12,900							+12,900
2000		142,500									+142,500
2013			90,000								+90,000
...											
2015			180,000								+180,000
...											
2025				77,000	6,000						+83,000
2027				12,900	6,000						+12,900
2028						19,320	2,052	2,384	23,756		

Discounted

Present worth (PW) in 1962
of costs in period:

Period											
1962–1980	330,580	265,123	85,443	74,231	5,201	0	176,168	78,973	12,112	78,016	1,105,847
Total 1981–2028 } at 7½%	0	0	9,126	9,032	615	59,966	63,165	6,709	7,794	0	156,407
1962–2028	330,580	265,123	94,569	83,263	5,816	59,966	239,333	85,682	19,906	78,016	1,262,254
1962–1980	322,035	243,575	80,046	72,469	5,108	0	165,105	75,999	10,924	76,621	1,051,882
Total 1981–2028 } at 8½%	0	0	6,419	6,473	442	47,582	47,279	5,022	5,834	0	119,051
1962–2028	322,035	243,575	86,465	78,842	5,350	47,582	212,384	81,021	16,758	76,621	1,170,933

a Operating and maintenance expenses of both hydro and thermal plant.
Note: The cash flow of costs does not include any transactions that are merely financial or accounting such as depreciation, amortization and interest. It includes only expenditures on goods and services in the year in which they are made. The hydro development results in a system using not only hydro but also some thermal plants.

TABLE 2: Cash Flow of Costs — Thermal Development — Lower Load

(monetary units)

Year	Investment						Operating expenses				Total
	Dam	Hydro units	Transmission 400 kv	Transmission 230 kv	Transmission 115 kv	Thermal plant	Production plant[a]	Fuel	Transmission	Frequency conversion	
Undiscounted											
1962							16,440	9,959			26,399
1963				14,000	2,000		16,440	11,086		30,000	73,526
1964				25,000	2,000		16,440	11,763		30,000	85,203
1965				38,000	2,000		16,440	13,695		30,000	100,135
1966						29,000	14,620	9,296	830		53,746
1967						59,000	14,620	10,704	830		85,154
1968						59,000	16,180	12,273	830		88,283
1969						59,000	17,740	13,382	830		90,952
1970						30,000	19,300	16,255	830		66,385
1971						29,000	20,860	17,895	830		68,585
1972						30,000	20,860	19,363	830		71,053
1973						29,000	22,420	19,836	830		72,086
1974						59,000	22,420	21,308	830		103,558
1975						59,000	23,980	25,434	830		109,244
1976						30,000	25,540	29,718	830		86,088
1977						29,000	27,100	31,542	830		88,472
1978						88,000	27,100	34,062	830		149,992
1979						89,000	28,660	39,904	830		158,394
1980						30,000	31,780	42,791	830		105,401
.. (1981)							33,340	54,631	830		88,801
1983						90,000					+90,000
1985						180,000					+180,000
..											

16

Cash flow of costs (undiscounted), by year

Year					Net flow
1995	77,000	6,000			+83,000
1998				90,000	+90,000
2000				90,000	
2002				90,000	
2004				90,000	
2006				90,000	
2008				90,000	+90,000
2010				180,000	+180,000
2013				90,000	+90,000
2015				180,000	+180,000
2025	77,000	6,000			+83,000
2028			33,340	54,631	830	88,801

Discounted

Present worth (PW) in 1962 of costs in period:

at 7½%									
1962–1980	0	0	65,245	5,201	326,567	206,207	183,062	5,298	78,016	870,196
Total 1981–2028	0	0	7,888	615	94,255	109,002	178,611	2,714	0	393,085
1962–2028	—	—	73,133	5,816	420,822	315,209	361,673	8,612	78,016	1,263,281
at 8½%									
1962–1980	0	0	63,890	5,108	296,348	191,739	168,133	5,396	76,621	807,235
Total 1981–2028	0	0	5,667	442	70,961	81,589	133,691	2,031	0	294,381
1962–2028	—	—	69,557	5,550	367,309	273,328	301,824	7,427	76,621	1,101,616

Note: The cash flow of costs does not include any transactions that are merely financial or accounting such as depreciation, amortization and interest. It includes only expenditures on goods and services in the year in which they are made.

TABLE 3: Summary of Present Worth of Costs
(Lower Load Development)

(thousands of monetary units)

Cost component	Period 1962–2028			Period 1962–1980			Period 1981–2028		
	Hydro Development	Thermal Development	Difference	Hydro Development	Thermal Development	Difference	Hydro Development	Thermal Development	Difference
				(present worth at 7½ per cent)					
Dam	331	—	331	331	—	331	—	—	—
Hydro units	265	—	265	265	—	265	—	—	—
Transmission 400 kv	95	—	95	85	—	85	10	—	10
Transmission 230 kv	83	73	10	74	65	9	9	8	1
Transmission 115 kv	6	6	—	5	5	—	1	1	—
Thermal plant	60	421	−361	—	327	−327	60	94	−34
Operating cost production plant	239	315	−76	176	206	−30	63	109	−46
Fuel	86	362	−276	79	183	−104	7	179	−172
Operating cost transmission	20	9	11	12	6	6	8	3	5
Frequency conversion	78	78	—	78	78	—	—	—	—
Total	1262	1263	−1	1106	870	236	156	393	−237
				(present worth at 8½ per cent)					
Dam	322	—	322	322	—	322	—	—	—
Hydro units	244	—	244	244	—	244	—	—	—
Transmission 400 kv	86	—	86	80	—	80	6	—	6
Transmission 230 kv	79	70	9	72	64	8	7	6	1
Transmission 115 kv	6	6	—	5	5	—	1	1	—
Thermal plant	48	367	−319	—	296	−296	48	71	−23
Operating cost production plant	212	273	−61	165	192	−27	47	81	−34
Fuel	81	302	−221	76	168	−92	5	134	−129
Operating cost transmission	17	7	10	11	5	6	6	2	4
Frequency conversion	77	77	—	77	77	—	—	—	—
Total	1171	1102	69	1052	807	245	119	295	−176

Note: For basic data see Tables 1 and 2.

it is possible to distinguish the influence of costs occurring in either period on the return obtained.

17.   Tables 1 and 2, and summary Table 3, also show the present worth of the cost flows if discounted at $8\frac{1}{2}\%$. Normally at least two calculations at different discount rates have to be made in order to arrive, by trial and error, at the rate which equalizes the present worth of the costs of the alternatives. These calculations also give a rough indication of what is a "significant" change in the underlying cost estimates. Table 3 shows, for example, that a difference in discount rate of one per cent (between $7\frac{1}{2}$ and $8\frac{1}{2}\%$) results in a difference of 80 thousand monetary units in the total present worth. By crude linear interpolation, this indicates that a difference of 35 thousand units in present worth is equivalent to a change of one-half of one per cent in the rate of return for variations around 8%.

18.   From Table 3, it is apparent that the outcome depends heavily on the present worth of the cost estimates of the dam, hydro units, thermal plants, fuel, and possibly operating cost of production plant. For instance, a 20% reduction in the cost of the dam would improve the return on the additional hydro investment by about one percentage point. A rise of close to 30% in the fuel price would have the same effect. It should be noticed that the "weights"—i.e. the present worth of the various cost items—decline at higher discount rates, so that somewhat greater percentage changes in costs are necessary to produce a change in the return of, say, one percentage point, than those indicated by the present worth figures obtained at $7\frac{1}{2}\%$. The effect is small, however, for small changes in the discount rate, except for items such as fuel costs where a large part of the difference in present worth between hydro and thermal alternatives occurs in the later years (1981–2026). Some of the other items— for example, the operating cost of the transmission lines—are small so that even a 50% change in the estimate affects the total present worth (and the return) only marginally. Others, such as investment in transmission (230 kv) and frequency conversion, are substantial, but any change in the cost estimates affects the thermal and hydro alternatives almost equally. Similarly the possible impact of under-

19

or overestimation of the large item "operating costs of production plant" may be much reduced by offsetting changes for both alternatives.[10]

19.   Offsetting items, in terms of present worth, may obviously result simply from the same item occurring in the same year in the basic cash flows of both alternatives. In practical application, such items would have been eliminated beforehand, (that is, before making the present worth calculations) in order to economize on computing time. Comparison of Tables 1 and 2 will show that this would eliminate the columns "transmission 115 kv" and "frequency conversion," and a good many items in the columns "transmission 230 kv" and "thermal plant."[10]Items of the same order of magnitude in the same year will similarly (largely) cancel out. Offsetting items in terms of present worth may also result, however, from the discounting process itself. Thus the difference in fuel costs is much reduced by the fact that costs are roughly the same for both alternatives in the early years and only differ greatly later on.

Different Cash Flows and the Use of Shadow Prices

20.   Costs different from those shown in the basic cash flows of Tables 1 and 2 may be due to under- or overestimation of physical inputs required, and/or of prices of inputs. Among the physical inputs, it is especially difficult to estimate accurately the input requirements of the dam. Difference of opinion is also possible on the fuel efficiency of thermal plants and other items. It will be clear by now, however, that the quantitative significance of such differences can easily be analyzed by reference to Table 3. If, for example, the operating costs of thermal plant (excluding fuel) had been systematically underestimated by 25%, their present worth at 7½%

---

[10] This is true if the under-estimate is due to the wage rate, affecting both alternatives. The error may be due, however, to different efficiency in use of labor in thermal plants, affecting mainly the thermal alternative (see paragraph 20). The same composite item "operating cost of production plant" in the cash flow of both alternatives is somewhat misleading as it refers largely to different costs—for thermal plants and hydro plants respectively. It would have been preferable to distinguish these in the cash flows.

would have to be adjusted upward by 25%, and this would be equivalent to an increase of about one per cent in the true return on the additional hydro investment. It also becomes easy to see, for example, that under-estimating labor efficiency in thermal plants by 20% in the period 1962–1980, and overestimating it by 10% in the later period 1981–2028, would result in raising the return by close to one-half of one per cent.

21.   Similarly, one can easily investigate the effect of using prices other than those used in the basic cash flows. There is bound to be some uncertainty in the estimates of future market prices. The analyst may also wish to determine the effect of using so-called "shadow prices"—for example, for foreign exchange, wage rates, fuel, etc.—if he has reason to think that market prices do not give a reasonable approximation of economic value to the country as a whole. To illustrate, what is the effect of a revision of the exchange rate downward by 20% on the return on hydro investment? The outcome depends, of course, on the foreign exchange component of the various cost items. Let us assume that in our example the foreign exchange components and thus the increases in costs resulting from lowering (devaluing) the exchange rate by 20% throughout the period 1962–2028, are as follows:

Item	Foreign exchange component	Increase in cost resulting from 20% lower foreign exchange rate
	per cent	per cent
Dam	50	10
Hydro units	80	16
Thermal units	75	15
Transmission	80	16
Other	0	0

22.   The cost of the hydro alternative in terms of present worth at 7½%, therefore, will rise by 10% of 331 (dam) *plus* 16% of 265 (hydro units) *plus* 16% of 105 (additional transmission) = 91;

and the cost of the thermal alternative in terms of present worth will rise by 15% of 361 (additional thermal plant) = 54. Thus the relative cost of the hydro alternative goes up by 37, and the return on the additional investment in hydro goes down by about one-half per cent.

23.   In similar fashion one can investigate whether a shadow wage rate for unskilled labor makes much difference to the return on the hydro investment. If, for example, unskilled labor amounts only to 2% of the total cost of the dam—which is an actual though probably extreme case—an adjustment in the wage rate can at most lower the cost of the dam by 2%—with a negligible effect on the return. In such a case it is, therefore, not necessary to devote time and energy to trying to find a proper value for the shadow wage rate of unskilled labor.

24.   The question may also arise whether the market price for cement is appropriate for the economic evaluation of the alternatives. Large over-capacity in a local cement industry may argue for using a lower price. Is this significant? Once again, it depends upon the "cement content" of the dam. If this is, say, 8%, a 12½% reduction in the cement price lowers the dam costs by one per cent, i.e. an insignificant amount. Relatively small adjustments in the cement price are therefore irrelevant. Even a 50% reduction in the cement price results only in 4% lower dam costs, and an increase of less than one-quarter of one per cent in the return on the investment in the hydro alternative.

25.   Thus the order of magnitude of the impact of various adjustments in input prices on the return can be established. This kind of sensitivity analysis brings out whether further refinement of the estimates made is worthwhile or not. Adjustments so small as not to affect the return calculation are irrelevant, and the analyst is better employed trying to estimate the crucial variables.

26.   As already pointed out above, one of the crucial variables in hydro/thermal comparisons is the price of fuel. In this particular case a 15% change upward or downward in the fuel price changes

the return of the additional hydro investment by approximately one-half of one per cent. The form of the analysis also permits experimentation with more complicated changes in fuel prices, varying over time.[11] If there is reason for thinking that fuel prices will later, say, from 1981 onward, be higher or lower than at present, the quantitative significance of this can easily be established.[12] Present fuel costs to the economy may be low because of over-capacity in fuel production itself or in transport facilities. In due course, over-capacity may disappear, or alternative uses may develop for a fuel such as natural gas, and a higher price may become appropriate. The present analysis can show how sensitive the return on the hydro investment is to such changes in fuel prices.

---

[11] In fact the basic data used in this study incorporate such changes in fuel prices over time.

[12] In our example, this is only convenient in two periods, 1962–1980 and 1981–2028, but a further breakdown by periods could, of course, easily have been provided.

IV

IMPACT OF
DIFFERENT GROWTH OF LOAD ON THE
RETURN ON THE ADDITIONAL HYDRO
INVESTMENT

Faster Growth of Demand for Electricity

27.   The return on the hydro investment will tend to be higher, of course, if the capacity of the dam can be fully utilized at an earlier date. The initial capital costs of the dam will then weigh less heavily on the hydro alternative. This is illustrated in Tables 4 and 5, which are similar to Tables 1 and 2 except that the system developments are geared to a more rapid rate of the growth of the power load (the "higher load"). As a result the capacity of the dam is fully utilized by 1979, and not by 1981 as in the previous example. Consequently the return on the additional hydro investment is somewhat higher, about 8¼%, as will be seen by comparing the figures for present worth of total cost, at 7½% and 8½% respectively, shown at the bottom of the tables. As explained above in paragraph 17, in practical application it is not necessary to recalculate all the data at an 8¼% discount rate, since interpolation between the 7½% and 8½% rates shows where the rate approximately lies.

TABLE 4: Cash Flow of Costs — Hydro Development — Higher Load

(monetary units)

	Investment						Operating expenses				Total
Year	Dam	Hydro units	Transmission 400 kv	Transmission 230 kv	Transmission 115 kv	Thermal plant	Production plant(a)	Fuel	Transmission	Frequency conversion	
Undiscounted											
1962	11,750						16,440	10,007			38,197
1963	23,600			14,000	2,000		16,440	11,178		30,000	97,218
1964	106,200			25,000	2,000		16,440	11,859		30,000	191,499
1965	147,500			38,000	2,000		16,440	13,719		30,000	247,659
1966	74,900	51,100					16,440	11,730	830		155,000
1967	43,300	57,200		12,900			16,440	13,588	830		144,258
1968	—		38,700				14,260	14,784	959		68,703
1969	—	51,100	51,500				16,220	4,740	959		124,519
1970	—	57,200	52,300				16,220	8,304	959		134,983
1971	—						16,520	2,052	2,384		20,956
1972		51,100					16,520	2,052	2,384		72,056
1973		57,200					16,520	3,572	2,384		79,676
1974		51,100					17,520	2,052	2,384		73,056
1975		57,200					17,520	2,052	2,384		79,156
1976		51,100					18,620	2,052	2,384		74,156
1977		57,200					18,620	2,052	2,384		80,256
1978							19,320	2,052	2,384		23,756
1979							19,320	2,052	2,384		23,756
1980							19,320	2,052	2,384		23,756

Year						
(1981)						
1983	90,000				←	+90,000
1985	180,000					+180,000
1995		77,000	6,000			+83,000
1997		12,900				+12,900
2000				142,500		+142,000
2013	90,000					+90,000
2015	180,000					+180,000
2025		77,000	6,000			+83,000
2027		12,900				+12,900
2028	19,320	2,052	2,384			23,756

Discounted

Present worth (PW) in 1962 of costs in period:

Period											
at 7½%											
1962–1978	330,580	273,282	85,443	74,231	5,201	0	168,490	84,476	10,766	78,016	1,110,485
1979–1980	0	0				0	10,906	1,158	1,346	0	13,410
1981–2028	0	0	9,126	9,032	615	59,966	63,165	6,709	7,794	0	156,407
Total 1962–2028	330,580	273,282	94,569	83,263	5,816	59,966	242,561	92,343	19,906	78,016	1,280,302
at 8½%											
1962–1978	322,035	251,618	80,046	72,469	5,108	0	158,847	81,332	9,780	76,621	1,057,856
1979–1980	0	0				0	9,276	985	1,145	0	11,406
1981–2028	0	0	6,419	6,473	442	47,582	47,279	5,022	5,834	0	119,051
Total 1962–2028	322,035	251,618	86,465	78,942	5,550	47,582	215,402	87,339	16,759	76,621	1,188,313

a Operating and maintenance expenses of both hydro and thermal plants.

Note: The cash flow of costs does not include any transactions that are merely financial or accounting such as depreciation, amortization and interest. It includes only expenditures on goods and services in the year in which they are made. The hydro development results in a system using not only hydro but also some thermal plants.

TABLE 5: Cash Flow of Costs — Thermal Development — Higher Load

(monetary units)

Year	Investment						Operating expenses				Total
	Dam	Hydro units	Transmission 400 kv	Transmission 230 kv	Transmission 115 kv	Thermal plant	Production plant	Fuel	Transmission	Frequency conversion	
Undiscounted											
1962							16,440	10,007			26,447
1963				14,000	2,000		16,440	11,178		30,000	73,618
1964				25,000	2,000		16,440	11,859		30,000	85,299
1965				38,000	2,000		16,440	13,719		30,000	100,159
1966						29,000	14,620	11,068	830		55,518
1967						59,000	14,620	12,832	830		87,282
1968						59,000	16,180	13,649	830		89,659
1968						59,000	17,740	14,590	830		92,160
1970						30,000	19,300	17,019	830		67,149
1971						29,000	20,860	19,239	830		69,929
1972						59,000	20,860	21,279	830		101,969
1973						59,000	22,420	22,592	830		104,842
1974						59,000	23,980	23,685	830		107,495
1975						59,000	25,540	26,937	830		112,307
1976						88,000	27,100	34,490	830		150,420
1977						89,000	28,660	40,143	830		158,633
1978						30,000	31,780	45,667	830		108,277
1979							33,340	52,875	830		87,045
1980							←	52,875	←		87,045

28

Cash flow of costs (rotated table):

Year							Total
(1981)				61,532		95,702	
1983		90,000					+90,000
1985		180,000					+180,000
1995	77,000	6,000					+83,000
1999		270,000					+270,000
2004		180,000					+180,000
2007		270,000					+270,000
2013		90,000					+90,000
2015		180,000					+180,000
2025							
2028	77,000	6,000	33,340	61,532	830	97,702	+830,000

Discounted

Present worth (PW) in 1962 of costs in period:

at 7½%								
1962–1978	65,245	5,201	343,104	193,009	175,357	5,429	78,016	865,361
1979–1980	0	0	0	18,820	29,848	469	0	49,137
1981–2028	7,888	615	97,610	109,002	201,173	2,714	0	419,002
Total 1962–2028	73,133	5,816	440,474	320,831	406,378	8,612	78,016	1,333,500
at 8¼%								
1962–1978	63,890	5,108	314,332	180,612	164,388	4,998	76,621	809,949
1979–1980	0	0	0	16,008	25,388	398	0	41,794
1981–2028	5,667	442	73,501	81,589	150,579	2,031	0	313,809
Total 1962–2028	69,557	5,550	387,833	278,209	340,355	7,427	76,621	1,165,552

Note: The cash flow of costs does not include any transactions that are merely financial or accounting such as depreciation, amortization and interest. It includes only expenditures on goods and services in the year in which they are made.

TABLE 6: Present Worth of Costs: Comparison of Higher and Lower Load Development, 1962–2028

(in thousands of monetary units)

Cost component	Hydro Development			Thermal Development			Difference (Hydro — Thermal)		
	Lower load (1)	Higher load (2)	Difference (2) — (1)	Lower load (1)	Higher load (2)	Difference (2) — (1)	Lower load (1)	Higher load (2)	Difference (2) — (1)
				(present worth at 7½ per cent)					
Dam	331	331	—	—	—	—	331	331	—
Hydro units	265	273	8	—	—	—	265	273	8
Transmission 400 kv	95	95	—	—	—	—	95	95	—
Transmission 230 kv	83	83	—	73	73	—	10	10	—
Transmission 115 kv	6	6	—	6	6	—	—	—	—
Thermal plant	60	60	—	421	441	20	−361	−381	−20
Operating cost production plant	239	243	4	315	321	6	−76	−78	−2
Fuel	86	92	6	362	406	44	−276	−314	−38
Operating cost transmission	20	20	—	9	9	—	11	11	—
Frequency conversion	78	78	—	78	78	—	—	—	—
Total	1262	1280	18	1263	1334	71	−1	54	−53
				(present worth at 8½ per cent)					
Dam	322	322	—	—	—	—	322	322	—
Hydro units	244	252	8	—	—	—	244	252	8
Transmission 400 kv	86	86	—	—	—	—	86	86	—
Transmission 230 kv	79	79	—	70	70	—	9	9	—
Transmission 115 kv	6	6	—	6	6	—	—	—	—
Thermal plant	48	48	—	367	388	21	−319	−340	−21
Operating cost production plant	212	215	3	273	278	5	−61	−63	−2
Fuel	81	87	6	302	340	38	−221	−253	−32
Operating cost transmission	17	17	—	7	7	—	10	10	—
Frequency conversion	77	77	—	77	77	—	—	—	—
Total	1170	1188	18	1102	1166	64	69	22	−46

Note: For basic data see Tables 1, 2, 4 and 5.

28.   Comparison of the present worth of cost components for the higher and lower load system developments (summarized in Table 6), indicates more precisely the reason for the greater return with the higher load. With more rapid growth of the load, the present worth of costs of hydro units rises somewhat for the hydro alternative, and the present worth of costs of thermal plant rises rather more for the thermal alternative. Operating expenses of production plant increase slightly for both alternatives, but largely cancel out. The most important difference, however, is the increase in fuel costs in the thermal alternative, offset only to a minor extent by an increase in fuel costs for the hydro alternative. The relative increase in fuel costs with higher load growth accounts for more than two-thirds of the total relative increase in cost (in terms of present worth) of the thermal alternative.

29.   From the general set-up of the problem—see paragraph 11 above—it might be thought that the period from 1981 onward does not play any role in these differences. It will be remembered that in the higher load growth variant, the system is kept at a constant level (for purpose of return calculations) from 1979 onward, the year in which full capacity of the dam is reached. And similarly, from 1981 onward for the lower variant. There may be further complications, however. Reference to Tables 1–6 shows that, in our example, about half the difference in fuel costs between the higher and the lower load developments occurs in the period 1981–2028. This results mainly from the higher load factor which, in this case, is associated with more rapid growth of the load. In terms of MW the systems are the same, after 1981, but the higher load growth happens to require more kilowatt-hours and, therefore, more fuel for the thermal alternative.[13] This effect is significant enough, in this case, to account for a difference of about one-quarter of one per cent in the return on additional hydro investment, between the higher and lower load curve (out of a total difference of about

---

[13] To a minor extent, the differences between higher and lower development are also due to the impossibility in the calculations of cutting off the expansion of the system at exactly the same point. A negligible difference results also from a slight shift forward in the replacement investments in thermal plant.

three-quarters of one per cent). A higher load factor is not an essential feature, however, of a faster rate of growth of the load. It depends on the reasons for the more rapid growth, i.e. on the growth of the components of the load. Conversely, different load factors may be associated with the same expansion of the load. A higher load factor tends, of course, to make the investment in the hydro alternative more attractive, as it raises the fuel costs of the thermal alternative while costs of the hydro alternative may remain the same. The quantitative significance of this can be analyzed along the lines previously indicated.

30.   The "pure" effect of a faster growth of the load on the return on additional hydro investment is small in our example—about one-half of one per cent. Given the many uncertainties of the estimates involved, it would appear therefore that a delay of two years in fully utilizing the dam—12 years rather than 10 years after the dam is finished—results in an insignificant difference in the return. In view of the fact that the underlying load projections used in this case[14] show the higher load in 1980 to be more than 25% higher than the lower load, this may be somewhat surprising. The explanation is to be found in the shape of the curves representing the growth of the load. In the remaining paragraphs we leave the case analyzed in paragraphs 15–30 and use various heavily stylized examples to illustrate the effect of differences in load growth on additional hydro investment.

Stylized Examples of Different Patterns of Load Growth

31.   Chart 2 depicts the basic patterns of load growth used in these stylized examples. In the case represented by Curve I, for example, the load rises from 500 MW in year zero ("the year of decision") to one thousand MW in year 5, in which the dam would be finished, and to 2,500 MW in year 25. This is described in this paper as a 20 year loading time. Tables 7 (a–b) show discounted cash flow calculations for simplified hydro and thermal developments

---

[14] See the table in Appendix A.

CHART 2
ILLUSTRATIVE PATTERNS OF LOAD GROWTH

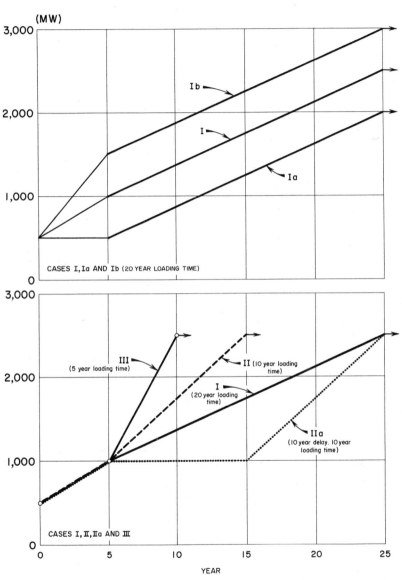

CASES I, Ia AND Ib (20 YEAR LOADING TIME)

CASES I, II, IIa AND III

III (5 year loading time)

II (10 year loading time)

I (20 year loading time)

IIa (10 year delay, 10 year loading time)

YEAR

IBRD – Economics Department
(R)2158

33

TABLE 7a: Different Patterns of Growth of Load:
Simplified Cash Flows of Alternative Hydro and Thermal Investments

(monetary units)

Year	Cases I, Ia and Ib, 20 year loading time							Case II, 10 year loading time				
	Load (MW)			Cost			Additional operating cost of thermal development	Load (MW)	Cost			Additional operating cost of thermal development
	I	Ia	Ib	Dam	Hydro units	Thermal units		MW	Dam	Hydro units	Thermal units	
0	500	500	500					500				
1	600	↑	700					600				
2	700		900					700				
3	800		1100					800				
4	900		1300					900				
5	1000	500	1500	1000	100	150		1000	1000	100	150	
6	1075	575	1575				5	1150				10
7	1150	650	1650		100	150	10	1300		100	150	20
8	1225	725	1725				15	1450				30
9	1300	800	1800		100	150	20	1600		100	150	40
10	1375	875	1875				25	1750				50
11	1450	950	1950		100	150	30	1900		100	150	60
12	1525	1025	2025				35	2050				70
13	1600	1100	2100		100	150	40	2200		100	150	80
14	1675	1175	2175				45	2350				90
15	1750	1250	2250		100	150	50	2500		150		100
16	1825	1325	2325				55	↑				←
17	1900	1400	2400		100	150	60					
18	1975	1475	2475				65					
19	2050	1550	2550		100	150	70					
20	2125	1625	2625				75					

34

21	2200	1700	2750
22	2275	1775	2775
23	2350	1850	2850
24	2425	1925	2925
25	2500	2000	3000
26			
65			

2500   2000   3000

Present worth (PW) in year 5 of cost in years:

	5–15	16–25	26–65	5–65
	1000	0	0	1000
at 8%	423	128	0	551
Total				

8 per cent

Internal rate of return on additional hydro investment:

[a] replacement investments

Assumptions:
1 thermal unit = 150 MW
Total capacity dam: 10 units = 1500 MW

100	150
100	150

year 35   150[a]
53 → 150[a]

634	192	82	908

80
85
90
95
100

100 → 2500

163	231	256	650

100

Life: thermal unit — 30 years
       hydro unit — 60 years
       dam—more than 60 years

Costs: dam: 1000
1 hydro unit: 100
1 thermal unit: 150

327
311
256
894

year 35   150[a] → 150[a]
44 →

1000	725	1087
0	0	0
0	0	108
1000	725	1195

10 per cent

Additional operating cost
(including fuel) of
thermal development: 1/15 per MW

TABLE 7b: Different Patterns of Growth of Load:
Simplified Cash Flows of Alternative Hydro and Thermal Investments   (*monetary units*)

| | Case IIa, 10 year delay, 10 year loading time | | | | | Case III, 5 year loading time | | | | |
| | Load | Cost | | | | Load | Cost | | | |
Year	MW	Dam	Hydro units	Thermal units	Additional operating cost of thermal development	MW	Dam	Hydro units	Thermal units	Additional operating cost of thermal development
0	500					500				
1	600					600				
2	700					700				
3	800					800				
4	900					900				
5	1000	[1000]^a				1000	1000	200	300	
6					68.3	1300		200	300	20
7					70.0	1600		200	300	40
8					71.7	1900		200	300	60
9					73.3	2200		200	300	80
10					75.0	2500		—	—	100
11					76.7			—	—	
12					78.3					
13					80.0					
14					81.7					
15	1000	[1000]^b	100	150	83.3					
16	1150		100	150	85.0					
17	1300		100	150	86.7					
18	1450		100	150	88.3					
19	1600		100	150	90.0					
20	1750		100	150	91.7					
21	1900		100	150	93.3					

22	2050	100	150	95.0
23	2200	100	150	96.7
24	2350	100	150	98.3
25	2500	—	—	100
26				

a)

year 45 →150^e →54 150^e

year 35 →300^e →39 300^e

| 65 | 2500 | | | 100 | 2500 | 100 |

Present worth (PW) in year 5 of costs in years:

	5–15	46	69	0	1000	862	1293	489
Total	16–25 } at 8%	289	434	151	0	0	0	311
	26–65	0	50	256	0	0	129	256
	5–65	335	553	407	1000	862	1422	1056

463^b · 0 · 0 · 463^b

Internal rate of return on
additional hydro investment: 6 per cent^a or 10 per cent^b   13¼ per cent

^a 1,000 if dam investment is made in year 5

^b 463 if dam investment is made in year 15

Assumptions:

1 thermal unit = 1 hydro unit = 150 MW
Total capacity dam: 10 units = 1500 MW

Life: thermal unit — 30 years
      hydro unit — 60 years
      dam—more than 60 years

Costs: dam: 1000
       1 hydro unit: 100
       1 thermal unit: 150

Additional operating cost
   (including fuel) of
   thermal development: 1/15 per MW

^c replacement investments

fitting the various cases represented in Chart 2. The dam is assumed to take 5 years to build, and to cost 1000 monetary units (all incurred for convenience sake in year 5), a hydro unit to cost 100, and a thermal unit 150. Additional cost (including fuel) of operating thermal plants rather than hydro units is assumed to be 1/15 per MW. Both thermal units and hydro units are 150 MW. Total capacity of the dam is 10 units or 1,500 MW. Lifetime of a thermal unit is 30 years, of a hydro unit 60 years, and of the dam more than 60 years. The same basic cost and size assumptions will be used throughout the remainder of the paper, unless otherwise noted.

32. The present worth calculation shows that the return on investment in hydro is about 8% if the load grows as represented by Curve I (see bottom of Case I, Table 7a). It should be noted that the return would also be 8%—as the cash flows would be exactly the same—if the load were to grow as in Curves Ia or Ib, their very different *rates* of growth notwithstanding. In Case Ia the load is static in the first five years but quadruples between years 5 and 25. In Case Ib it increases rapidly in the first five years, but between years 5 and 25 it only doubles. Calculated from year zero, on the other hand, the rate of growth of Ib is much greater than that of Ia. Case I is intermediate between these two extremes. These differences in rates of growth are irrelevant, however; what counts is the *absolute* increase in the load from the year that the dam is finished, *not* from the time the estimate is made or the construction of the dam is started. In our example, the absolute growth of the load after year 5 determines the speed with which the dam can be "loaded."[15] The much greater absolute increase in Case Ib between year 0 and

---

[15] The loading time of the dam does not depend solely on the growth of the load. Possible replacements of existing thermal plants may provide additional scope for using hydro power, and thus shortening the time needed for the dam to get fully loaded. The importance of this factor depends, of course, on the age structure of existing plant in year 0. Thermal plants installed during the construction period of the dam (cf. note 15 below) only play a role in this if the loading time of the dam is very long (more than 25 years); otherwise their replacement affects both the thermal and hydro developments equally. The effect of "replacement load bonuses" on the return can be analyzed by simply adding them to the growth in the load derived from estimates of future demand for power.

5, i.e. during the construction period, does not help.[16] The absolute annual increases after year 5 are the same in all three Cases, I, Ia and Ib; hence the return is the same on the additional hydro investment.[17]

33.   Obviously, it is not simply a question of the total loading time, but also of the shape of the load growth curve. Curves I, II and IIa (cf. Chart 2) all show an increase by 1,500 MW between year 5 and 25.[18] However, investment in hydro is obviously more advantageous in Case II: discounted at 8% the present worth of costs of thermal power far exceeds that of hydro power. Experimentation shows that the internal rate of return is about 10%. Case IIa is obviously the worst—if it were decided to put in the dam immediately, although needed only 10 years later, the return would be only 6%. Case IIa is indeed a textbook example of the need for postponing the investment: if construction is postponed by 10 years so that the dam is ready in year 15, the pattern of loading is the same as in Case II, and so is the internal return of 10% (i.e., higher than for Case I).[19]

---

[16] Different rates of growth of load during the construction period affect, of course, the need for additional power capacity in the interim period. Our heavily stylized examples assume that this does not significantly affect the system development from year 5 onward. The faster rate of growth in the interim period is not necessarily an advantage; it may absorb existing excess capacity; it may also necessitate new investment in excess of load requirements in year 5.

[17] These considerations also caution against overestimating the influence on the return of an increase in the service area by interconnection. In comparing growth of the interconnected and the non-interconnected load, it should be noticed that the starting point of the former is higher. The gap between the two loads after, say, 10 years, overestimates, therefore, the difference in their absolute increases by this difference in starting level.

[18] Strictly speaking, these curves have a different loading time: 20 years in Case I, 10 years in Case II and 5 years in Case III. Cases II and III may be thought of, however, as "exaggerated" examples of load curves rapidly rising in the early years and flattening out later, so that they also get fully loaded only after 20 years.

[19] This does *not* mean that Cases II and IIa are equally good hydro investments. If the rate of interest is, say, 8%, the cost advantage of hydro over thermal is much larger in Case II than in Case IIa, as may be verified by comparing the figures shown at the bottom of Table 7. This simply reflects that, in that case, a return of 10% as of now is better than the same return as of 10 years later.

CHART 3

RELATIONSHIP BETWEEN RATE OF RETURN ON INVESTMENT IN HYDRO AND LENGTH OF LOADING TIME OF DAM

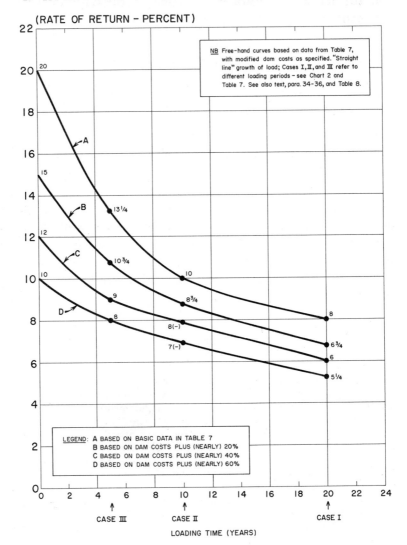

(RATE OF RETURN – PERCENT)

NB Free-hand curves based on data from Table 7, with modified dam costs as specified. "Straight line" growth of load; Cases I, II, and III refer to different loading periods – see Chart 2 and Table 7. See also text, para. 34-36, and Table 8.

LEGEND: A BASED ON BASIC DATA IN TABLE 7
B BASED ON DAM COSTS PLUS (NEARLY) 20%
C BASED ON DAM COSTS PLUS (NEARLY) 40%
D BASED ON DAM COSTS PLUS (NEARLY) 60%

CASE III   CASE II   CASE I

LOADING TIME (YEARS)

IBRD – Economics Department
(2R) 2159

40

34.   As shown just above, shortening of the loading time of the dam from 20 years (Case I) to 10 years (Case II) raises the return in this example from 8% to 10%. Further shortening of the loading time to 5 years (Case III) raises the return further to about 13¼%. Clearly, the maximum return is reached in the case of instantaneous loading of the dam in year 5. In that case additional investment in the hydro alternative of 1000 + 1000 − 1500 = 500 gives savings in operating costs of 100 per annum "forever after,"[20] i.e. a return of (nearly) 20%. These results are presented graphically in Curve A of Chart 3 which is suggestive of the relationship existing between the loading time (with roughly straight-line load growth) and the return on the additional investment in hydro power. The impact on the return of a year's delay in reaching the full capacity of the dam becomes less the longer it takes. At the level of a loading time of 5 years one year sooner or later is equivalent, in this example, to a difference in the return of the order of one per cent. But around a 10 year loading time it takes a delay of roughly 2 years, and at a level of 15 years a delay of some 4 years, to have a similar effect. This seems to suggest that small differences in rates of growth, both of which result in the dam reaching full capacity beyond, say, 10 years, are not very important. The return appears not to be very sensitive to such differences in the load growth. Much more importance, of course, attaches to what happens in the early years.

Effect of Different Cost Data

35.   The particular result obtained here depends, of course, on the cost data used in this example.[21] With different cost data for the dam, hydro units, thermal plants, and/or additional operating cost of thermal plant, the return on hydro investment—and the sensitivity of the return to changes in loading time—will be different. For example, if the dam costs are raised by nearly 40%, the maximum return, at instantaneous loading, drops sharply from 20% to 12%. But a 10 year loading period then gives a return of nearly 8%

---

[20] Neglecting the replacement cost of thermal plants in year 35.
[21] And, on the assumption of straight-line load growth; see paras. 37–38 below.

(as compared with 10% before) and a 20 year loading period gives a return of about 6% (as compared with 8% before). This is illustrated by Curve C in Chart 3, which also shows the returns obtaining at different loading times if dam costs are raised by nearly 20% (Curve B) and by nearly 60% (Curve D). These results are derived from Table 8, showing, at different rates of discount, the present worth of the hydro and thermal development costs in Cases I, II and III. These results suggest that investments in hydro alternatives with lower maximum ("instantaneous loading") returns are much less sensitive to delays in fully loading the dam capacity, but that the difference is small for loading times beyond 10 years.

TABLE 8: Rate of Return by Different Loading Times for Changes in Cost of the Dam

(monetary units)

Cost components	\multicolumn{9}{c}{Present worth at}								
	14%	12%	11%	10%	9%	8%	7%	6%	5%
Case I (20 year loading time)									
Hydro development									
Dam						1007	1117	1382	1710
Hydro units						551	586	625	672
Thermal development									
Thermal units						908	973	1100	1241
Additional operating cost						650	730	907	1141
Case II (10 year loading time)									
Hydro development									
Dam				1008	1137	1364			
Hydro units				676	700	725			
Thermal development									
Thermal units				1072	1129	1195			
Additional operating cost				612	708	894			
Case III (5 year loading time)									
Hydro development									
Dam	973	1058	1148		1390	1616			
Hydro units	782	807	820		848	862			
Thermal development									
Thermal units	1196	1250	1283		1367	1422			
Additional operating cost	559	615	685		871	1056			

Note: Dam costs vary: the other costs are given. Cases I, II, and III refer to "straight line" loading times of 20, 10 and 5 years respectively. Cf. Chart 2 and Table 7. Basic cost data as in para. 31, and Table 7. Dam costs are varied, as described in para. 35; the resulting effect on the rate of return emerges from the table. For example, with dam costs at 1000, the rate of return, in Case I, is 8 per cent (1000 + 551 = 908 + 650 approximately). With dam costs nearly 40 per cent higher, at 1382, the return falls to 6 per cent (1382 + 625 = 1100 + 907).

36. A further check was made of the influence of different proportions of the four major categories of costs distinguished here on the return on hydro investment for different loading times. (See Table 9).

TABLE 9: Rate of Return by Different Loading Times for Changes in Proportions of Cost Components

(monetary units)

Components	Basic cost data from Table 7	Modified cost data *a*	*b*
	Instantaneous loading (PW at 20 per cent)		
Hydro development			
Dam	1000	1383	1383
Hydro units	1000	1000	1000
Thermal development			
Thermal units	1507	1883	1507
Additional operating cost	500	500	875
Rate of return	20%	20%	20%
	Case I (20 year loading time, PW at 8 per cent)		
Hydro development			
Dam	1000	1383	1383
Hydro units	551	551	551
Thermal development			
Thermal units	908	1135	908
Additional operating cost	650	650	1135
Rate of return	8%	c. 7¼%	c. 8½%
	Case II (10 year loading time, PW at 10 per cent)		
Hydro development			
Dam	1000	1383	1383
Hydro units	676	676	676
Thermal development			
Thermal units	1072	1340	1072
Additional operating cost	612	612	1071
Rate of return	10%	c. 9½%	c. 10½%
	Case III (5 year loading time, PW at 14 per cent)		
Hydro development			
Dam	1000	1383	1383
Hydro units	782	782	782
Thermal development			
Thermal units	1196	1495	1196
Additional operating cost	559	559	980
Rate of return	13½%	c. 12¾%	c. 14%

a dam cost, *plus* 38 per cent; thermal unit cost, *plus* 25 per cent
b dam cost, *plus* 38 per cent; additional operating cost of thermal development, plus 75 per cent
Note: See text, para. 36 for explanation. Cases I, II, and III refer to "straight-line" loading times of 20, 10 and 5 years respectively. Cf. Chart 2 and Table 7. Present worth data at discount rate approximately "right" for Case considered; the "weight" of cost increases varies with this discount rate.

Obviously, an "instantaneous loading" return of, for example, 20% as yielded by our basic data, could also be obtained if an increase in the cost of the dam by, say, nearly 40% were offset by an increase in cost of thermal plant (by about 25% per unit), or additional operating costs of the thermal development (by about 75% per MW). Perhaps more surprisingly, the shape of the curves showing, for these changed cost data, the relationship between the rate of return on additional hydro investment and the length of the loading time is not very different from those shown in Chart 3. If the increase in dam costs is offset by higher costs of thermal plant, so as to yield the same instantaneous loading return, returns for longer loading times tend to be somewhat lower than before; if offset by higher additional operating cost of thermal development, returns for longer loading times tend to be somewhat higher than before.[22] Both differences are small, however,—amounting to very roughly one-half of one per cent from the original rate of return—and the three curves run roughly parallel from year 5 onward, at least over the relevant range of years. This suggests that the instantaneous loading rate of return—which can always speedily be calculated— gives a useful indication of the return for longer loading times. Thus it becomes possible to see how critical the demand projection is for the outcome of the return calculation.

Curvilinear Growth of Load

37. The load curves considered so far have one feature in common: they all show growth in constant straight-line fashion from the time of completion of the dam over the relevant range until the dam is fully loaded.[23] Some impression of the return on additional hydro

---

[22] The explanation seems to be the following: longer loading time tends to lower costs, in terms of present worth, because costs are delayed, but to raise them because the discount rate (internal return) becomes lower. On balance, this lowers the cost of thermal plant, in terms of present worth, and raises the additional operating cost of thermal development; cf. Table 9. For "fuel," the "discount rate" effect outweighs the "delay effect," as the bulk of the cost occurs in later years. Thus an increase in cost of thermal plant, sufficient to compensate "instantaneously" an increase in dam costs, falls short if the loading time is longer—so that the return on hydro is relatively lower than on the original data. And vice versa for additional operating cost of thermal development.

[23] This applies also to Case IIa with the exception that the starting point of its growth is delayed by 10 years after completion of the dam.

CHART 4

RETURN ON HYDRO INVESTMENT FOR
DIFFERENT LOAD GROWTH

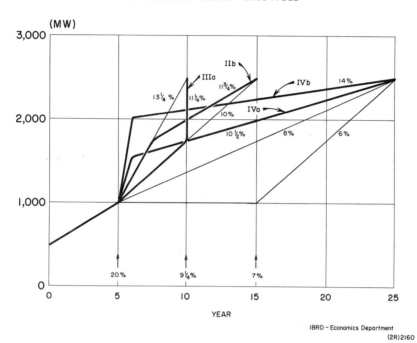

IBRD – Economics Department
(2R)2160

Note: Thin lines represent Cases I, II, IIa, and III of Chart 2 and Table 7. Thick lines represent the new "curvilinear" Cases IIb, IIIa, IVa, and IVb. Respective rates of return (based on cost data of Table 7) are written in alongside. Rates of return written in along horizontal axis refer to instantaneous loading of dam capacity in year indicated. See text, para. 37–38.

investment with load curves having "curvilinear" expansion paths may be obtained by inspection. It is obvious, for example, that growth of the load intermediate between the cases represented in Chart 2 will result in an "intermediate" return on the additional investment in hydro. The results of some experiments along these lines are shown in Chart 4. Thin lines represent the previous Cases, I, II, IIa and III, with their respective rates of return (based on the basic cost data of Table 7) written in alongside. Cases IIb and IIIa, intermediate between II and III, have a return of about 11¾% and 11¼% respectively, as compared with 10% for Case II and

45

TABLE 10a: Some Stylized Curvilinear Patterns of Load Growth: Simplified Cash Flows

(monetary units)

	Case IIb, 10 year loading time, early growth of load					Case IIIa, 5-year loading time, late growth of load				
	Load	Cost				Load	Cost			
Year	MW	Dam	Hydro units	Thermal units	Additional operating cost of thermal development	MW	Dam	Hydro units	Thermal units	Additional operating cost of thermal development
0	500					500				
1	600					600				
2	700					700				
3	800					800				
4	900					900				
5	1000	1000	200	300		1000	1000	100	150	
6	1300		200	300	20	1150		100	150	10
7	1600		200	300	40	1300		100	150	20
8	1800		100	150	53.3	1450		100	150	30
9	1900		100	150	60	1600		600	900	40
10	2000				66.6	2500				100
11	2100		100	150	73.3					
12	2200		100	150	80					
13	2300				86.6					
14	2400				93.3					
15	2500				100					
16										
17										
18										
19										
20										

46

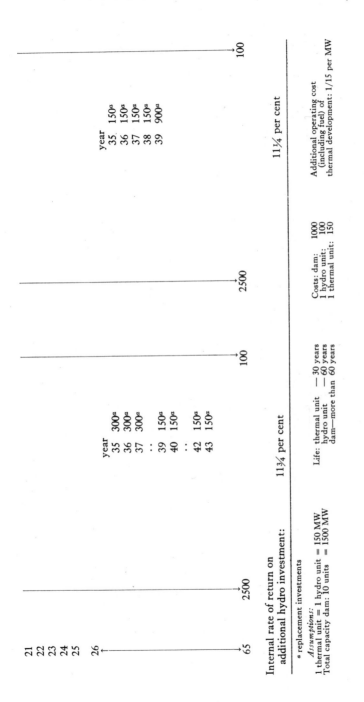

year	
35	150ᵃ
36	150ᵃ
37	150ᵃ
38	150ᵃ
39	900ᵃ

year	
35	300ᵃ
36	300ᵃ
37	300ᵃ
: :	
39	150ᵃ
40	150ᵃ
: :	
42	150ᵃ
43	150ᵃ

Internal rate of return on
additional hydro investment: 11¾ per cent   11¼ per cent

ᵃ replacement investments

Assumptions:
1 thermal unit = 1 hydro unit = 150 MW
Total capacity dam: 10 units = 1500 MW

Life: thermal unit — 30 years
hydro unit — 60 years
dam—more than 60 years

Costs: dam: 1000
1 hydro unit: 100
1 thermal unit: 150

Additional operating cost
(including fuel) of
thermal development: 1/15 per MW

47

TABLE 10b: Some Stylized Curvilinear Patterns of Load Growth:
Simplified Cash Flows

(monetary units)

| | Case IVa, 20 year loading time, early growth of load | | | | | Case IVb, 20 year loading time, jump in growth in year 6 | | | | |
| | Load | Cost | | | | Load | Cost | | | |
Year	MW	Dam	Hydro units	Thermal units	Additional operating cost of thermal development	MW	Dam	Hydro units	Thermal units	Additional operating cost of thermal development
0	500					500				
1	600					600				
2	700					700				
3	800					800				
4	900					900				
5	1000	1000	400	600		1000	1000	100	1050	
6	1550				36.6	2025				68.3
7	1600		100	150	40.0	2050		100	150	70.0
8	1650				43.3	2075				71.7
9	1700				46.6	2100				73.3
10	1750		100	150	50.0	2125				75.0
11	1800				53.3	2150				76.7
12	1850				56.6	2175				78.3
13	1900		100	150	60.0	2200		100	150	80.0
14	1950				63.3	2225				81.7
15	2000				66.6	2250				83.3
16	2050		100	150	70.0	2275				85.0
17	2100				73.3	2300				86.7
18	2150				76.6	2325				88.3
19	2200		100	150	80.0	2350		100	150	90.0
20	2250				83.3	2375				91.7

21	2300						93.3
22	2350			100	150	2400	95.0
23	2400					2425	96.7
24	2450					2450	98.3
25	2500					2475	100.0
26						2500	

86.6
90.0
93.3
96.6
100.0

year 35 1050ᵃ
: :
37 150ᵃ
: :
43 150ᵃ
: :
49 150ᵃ

year 35 600ᵃ
: :
37 150ᵃ
: :
40 150ᵃ
: :
43 150ᵃ
: :
46 150ᵃ
: :
49 150ᵃ
: :
52 150ᵃ

2500 → 100 → 2500 → 100

65 ← 2500

Internal rate of return on additional hydro investment: 10½ per cent   14 per cent

ᵃ replacement investments

Assumptions:

1 thermal unit = 1 hydro unit = 150 MW
Total capacity dam: 10 units = 1500 MW

Life: thermal unit — 30 years
hydro unit — 60 years
dam—more than 60 years

Costs: dam: 1000
1 hydro unit: 100
1 thermal unit: 150

Additional operating cost (including fuel) of thermal development: 1/15 per MW

13¼% for Case III.[24] It should be noted that the return in Case IIb is higher than in Case IIIa, although its "loading time" is longer—10 years rather than 5 years; this is outweighed by the higher load in the early years.

38. A somewhat more difficult exercise, perhaps, is to guess the return on additional hydro investment in cases which "cross over" the straight-line growth cases. Cases IVa and IVb have rapid initial growth of the load, and small increases thereafter, so as to reach full capacity only after 20 years. Once again, the importance of the early years stands out. Case IVa has about the same return as Case II, and Case IVb roughly the same return as Case III, although the respective loading times of Cases IVa and IVb are much longer. Inversely, the influence of slow initial growth of the load and rapid increases later, can be seen by comparing them with benchmarks of the return on additional hydro investment in extreme cases of "delayed instantaneous loading"—shown along the horizontal axis of Chart 4. It is apparent that rapid increases in the load after, say, 10 years, have only a marginal effect on the return.

_____

[24] The basic data for Cases IIb and IIIa and other curvilinear cases referred to below are given in Table 10 (a–b).

V

SUMMARY AND CONCLUSIONS

39.   This paper has demonstrated a systematic and logically correct method for comparing the economic merits of alternative power developments. It has shown how the different cost streams involved can be compared by discounting them to obtain their present values, and it has indicated the critical nature of the discount rate used. It has noted that the discount (interest) rate which makes the present values of two alternative cost streams equal is a measure of the return on the additional investment in one system (hydro). This return results from the savings in operating costs for the life of the project over those in the alternative thermal system. It has shown how to appraise the sensitivity of this return to changes in key data of costs and demand. In particular, it has illustrated a convenient way of assessing the impact of changes in individual cost items on the return by breaking down the usual discounted cash flow calculations by cost components and periods. In this way the sensitivity of return calculations to different estimates of input requirements or input prices can readily be seen and the crucial cost variables can be identified.

40. While variations in the estimated value of inputs—dam, generating equipment, fuel, labor, etc.—can be made in the cost streams of alternative power developments without changing the timing and capacity of the projected investments, this is not the case with variations in the estimated growth of the market. A more rapid expansion of the market will tend to favor a hydro over a thermal development but the actual effect of a given increase in the growth of demand can only be determined by working out the consequences in terms of a changed pattern of investment. Because the market is a very important and often uncertain element in the appraisal and because the effect of changes in market estimates are not readily evident, it is most desirable to be able to know the approximate effect of such changes on the return calculations in advance—again, in order to identify their importance before devoting effort to the often laborious task of replanning the development of the system.

41. An attempt to work out some rough rules of thumb for this purpose has been made in this paper. This has been done through the use of simplified examples of hydro-thermal comparisons which assume that the hydro facilities (the dam) are loaded to capacity over different periods of time. The maximum rate of return is obtained, of course, on the extreme and convenient assumption that the load grows fast enough to make possible the full utilization of the dam's capacity immediately on its completion. Tentatively it emerges from the analysis that this maximum rate is a good benchmark from which to estimate the lower returns obtained with slower rates of growth. For simple straight-line growth curves the return drops fairly rapidly and regularly from this maximum rate as the period required for full loading is extended. After 10 years the effect on the return of delays of a year rapidly becomes negligible. Different cost structures appear to have only a small influence on these relationships between the rate of return and the loading time. In the case of less simple load-growth curves it is much more difficult to generalize, but the examples presented give some idea of what may be expected.

APPENDIX A

THE GURI PROJECT

1. In 1962 the Venezuelan Government asked the Bank to consider the technical and economic justification for the first stage of a large hydroelectric installation at Guri on the Caroni river, the principal tributary of the Orinoco. The Guri project was considered an important step in the development of the Guayana region, sparsely populated but rich in minerals, including high quality iron ore, oil, gas and coal. A large industrial development was planned. Consultants proposed the construction of the project in several stages. By 1968, there would be in operation a concrete gravity-type dam, two generators of 175 MW each, and a double circuit 230 kv transmission line about 80 km long connecting them with the earlier Macagua hydroelectric station. Eight additional units would be installed later to provide, around 1980, a total capacity of 1750 MW from Guri.

2. The potential market consisted, apart from the Guayana, of the Caracas, Central and Eastern areas. The largest system, serving Caracas with a capacity of 450 MW, was an independently managed and wholly thermal 50 cycle system which would have to be converted to 60 cycles before it could be effectively interconnected.

This interconnection was to be the responsibility of the authorities, who proposed to lay some 600 km of 230 kv transmission line, plus an extra high voltage (400 kv) connection to Caracas, coming into service at different dates.

3.   The size of the market appeared critical. Two estimates of demand were made, a higher and a lower, both forecasting a considerable increase in load. The higher estimate was mainly dependent on more optimistic calculations of the speedy development of Guayana, and particularly of an earlier development of aluminum for export. It will be seen from the table below that the two estimates did not diverge greatly until about 1980, when the higher was more than 25 per cent above the lower one:

Preliminary load forecasts, (1961), Venezuela
(peak demand at generating plant, in MW)

	1962	1968	1975	1980
Lower estimate	669	1087	1833	2612
Higher estimate	675	1105	1974	3307

4.   The scale of such projections of demand, together with the existence in Venezuela of considerable supplies of natural gas, suggested the need for a careful assessment of the alternative of a mainly thermal system. The Bank studied two alternatives from the point of view of the national economy:

   a) one with the hydroelectric Guri project, but including some new thermal plant;

   b) one in which the only new plant added would be thermal.

In both cases, a fully interconnected system was assumed, but in the thermal case, there would of course be no requirement for the 400 kv direct transmission line from Guri nor for some of the 230 kv lines. It was necessary to make new price estimates for natural gas in the economic analysis of the thermal alternative, since existing prices, under dispute, represented a completely different demand structure from that which would prevail.

5. The mission projected the investment and operating costs of the two alternative systems to the year in which the forecasts indicated that the 1750 MW capacity of Guri, as a section of the total capacity in the hydroelectric system alternative, would be fully loaded. This would be in 1979 on the higher load estimate and in 1981 on the lower estimate.

6. The discount rates which equalize the present worth of the cost streams of development with and without Guri are shown below for the higher and lower load forecasts respectively, and for two different cost assumptions:

Rate of return on the extra investment cost in the Guri scheme (per cent)

Cost assumption	Load forecast	
	Higher	Lower
Mission cost estimates for gas and operating labor; consultants' estimate of costs for Guri	8¼	7½
Mission cost estimates for gas and operating labor; consultants' estimate of costs for Guri increased 20%	6½	6

If existing contract prices for gas, and current operating labor costs, were used, this 8¼ per cent rose to 10 per cent.

7. The mission *concluded:*
   1) that the most optimistic yield estimate of 8¼ per cent on the additional investment in hydro was on the low side under Venezuelan conditions, particularly in view of the many uncertainties in the projections of demand;
   2) that the early development of Guri could not be justified unless the Caracas load were included in the system, including conversion to a 60 cycle system;

3) it was also noted that a thermal-based system was inherently more flexible. The yields, of course, would be considerably improved, and the uncertainties underlying them reduced, if construction of Guri were delayed by a period of between 5 and 10 years. The yields would also be considerably increased if a very large aluminum plant were to come into production in the early 1970's instead of in 1979–80 as forecast.

8.   Subsequently agreement was reached to convert the Caracas system to 60 cycles. In addition, new specific arrangements for industrial development and the inclusion of new market areas led to new estimates of demand with a higher projection for the earlier years and a somewhat lower one for the later years. These made the Guri project a more attractive investment than appeared from the original calculations. In 1963 the Bank made a loan of $85 million toward the estimated project cost of $137 million.

APPENDIX B

Table of Contents

A NOTE ON THE TREATMENT OF JOINT
COSTS IN THE ECONOMIC EVALUATION
OF MULTIPURPOSE PROJECTS

I.

INTRODUCTION

1.   The purpose of this note is to clarify the special issues that arise in cost-benefit analysis when some costs are shared between two or more projects. The financial problem of how to allot these joint costs equitably between various users or government budgetary accounts is not discussed.

2.   In these somewhat stylized examples, a choice has to be made between the following alternatives: simple dam irrigation, simple hydroelectric scheme, tube well irrigation, thermal power, and a multipurpose project combining dam irrigation with hydro power and costing less than these two projects separately. Thermal and hydro power, and dam and tube well irrigation, are assumed to be mutually exclusive alternatives.

Appendix Table 1

Project	Investment costs (discounted)	Benefits (discounted)	Net present worth
Dam irrigation	100	90	−10
Hydro power	80	86	6
Multipurpose			
(dam irrigation & hydro)	150	176	26
Tube wells	50	58	8
Thermal power	40	54	14
(Tube well + thermal	90	112	22)

Note: Benefits are taken net of current costs

3. Tube well irrigation is here preferable to simple dam irrigation, as its net present worth is greater. Similarly thermal power is superior to simple hydro power. But the multipurpose project, through its savings of 30 in joint costs (total costs are only 150, rather than 100 + 80) is superior to a combination of tube well irrigation and thermal power, with a net present worth of 26 against 18. Thus while each individual project would be more expensive than its alternative, the combination of the two may be economically justified by sharing of costs.

4. In principle, the existence of joint costs raises little difficulty. All relevant costs and benefits must be summed and evaluated. In practice, analysts have often been led astray by the actual complexities of the situation.

II.

SOME COMMON ERRORS

Additional investment methods

5. In one type of calculation, the additional investment necessary to obtain the hydroelectric benefits of the multipurpose project is compared with the thermal power alternative, all joint costs being allocated to dam irrigation. This gives the following result:

Project	Investment costs (discounted)	Benefits (discounted)	Net present worth
Additional hydro investment	150–100 = 50	86	36
Thermal power	40	54	14

The additional investment in hydro facilities shows a higher return in terms of net present worth than the thermal alternative (86 − 50 > 14). The conclusion might therefore be drawn that the multipurpose project should be favored, especially since it has a positive net present worth. However, the only comparison made is one between dam plus hydro (multipurpose) and dam plus thermal (26 > −10 + 14). It does not take sufficient account of the alternative irrigation project. For example, if the net present worth of tube well investment were not 8 but 14, the combined net present worth of thermal and tube well investment would be 28, which exceeds that of the dam irrigation and hydro multipurpose project. Similarly, in the absence of a tube well alternative, if the net present worth of thermal investment were 28, it also would give a higher return than the multipurpose project.

6. A variant of the additional investment error is a method which arrives at these additional investment costs by deducting the value of the discounted benefits of dam irrigation from the total discounted cost of the multipurpose project. Appendix Table 3 illustrates, with figures different from those in Tables 1 and 2.

Appendix Table 3

Project	Investment costs (discounted)	Benefits (discounted)	Net present worth
Dam irrigation	100	118	18
Hydro power	80	63	−17
Multipurpose	150	181	31
Thermal power	40	56	16

The discounted benefits from irrigation in the above example amount to 118, and the net additional investment costs of hydro power are therefore put at $150 - 118 = 32$. On this basis, the net present worth of investment in hydro power is $63 - 32 = 31$, which is greater than in thermal power (16). The conclusion is therefore drawn, erroneously, that the multipurpose project should be adopted. In fact what this procedure compares is the net present worth of the multipurpose project (31) and the thermal project value (16).[1] It ignores other alternatives including the best solution in this case, a combination of dam irrigation and thermal power $(18 + 16 = 34)$.

Arbitrary Allocation of Joint Costs

7. Another calculation allocates the joint costs in an essentially arbitrary manner among the components. Thus in Appendix Table 1, the joint costs of the dam and hydro projects, amounting to 30 $(100 + 80 - 150)$,[2] might be split on a fifty-fifty basis between the dam part and the hydro part and added to their specific (i.e. non-joint) costs. The investment costs of dam irrigation are then calculated as $150 - 80 + 15 = 85$, and of the hydro project as $150 - 100 + 15 = 65$. Or the total costs are split fifty-fifty, so that the investment cost of both dam irrigation and hydro power are each put at 75. Both ways, or any other variant, are arbitrary. Thus, the first way shows the hydroelectric project, taken by itself, as a better project than thermal power $(86 - 65 = 21 > 14)$, and the second as worse $(86 - 75 = 11 < 14)$. In the irrigation comparison, it is the other way round; the dam appears a worse project than tube wells in the first case $(90 - 85 = 5 < 8)$ and a better one in the second $(90 - 75 = 15 > 8)$. Clearly it is a matter of chance whether the comparison of the individual parts in this way gives the right answer.

---

[1] The true net present worth of the additional hydro investment is $31 - 18 = 13$.

[2] If preferred, joint costs may be correctly thought of as investment costs of multipurpose project less (additional investment costs of hydro + additional investment costs of irrigation) or $150 - (50 + 70) = 30$.

8. Comparison in Appendix Table 1 between the multipurpose project as a whole and tube well irrigation plus thermal power shows the former to give a better return (26 > 22). This is significant but not necessarily decisive, however. For instance, if discounted benefits of tube well irrigation were 21 and of thermal power 1, their combined benefits would still be 22 and the comparison would still be true; yet a combination of hydro power and tube wells would be even better (6 + 21> 26). Or, with the discounted costs of the hydroelectric project 10 lower and the discounted benefits of tube well irrigation 10 higher, thermal power plus tube wells is a better investment than the multipurpose project (14 + 18 > 26),[3] but again hydro power plus tube wells are better still (16 + 18> 32). All relevant comparisons need to be made to arrive consistently at the right investment decision.

---

[3] The change in hydro costs affects only the net present worth of the hydro project, *not* that of the multipurpose project.

III.

SYSTEMATIC CONSIDERATION OF ALTERNATIVES

9. The full array of alternative projects and project combinations can readily be seen by setting out the net present worth of the single purpose projects as in Appendix Table 4 below. Using again the basic data of Appendix Table 1, there are two (mutually exclusive) single purpose projects, in each of two sectors, irrigation and power. If the higher value is underlined in each sector and the two values added (in this case tube wells and thermal), the best combination of single-purpose projects will be determined and its net present worth can be inserted in the third column.

Appendix Table 4

Projects	Irrigation		Power		Best combination or single project
Single purpose	Dam	−10	Hydro	6	
	Tube wells	8	Thermal	14	22
Multipurpose					26

10. This net present worth can then be compared with that of the multipurpose project. If it is less, (which would always be the case if dam plus hydro is the best combination under the single-purpose heading), then the multipurpose project is to be preferred.

11. It may be that one single purpose project will have a higher net present worth than any combination. This will happen if both single purpose projects in one sector have a negative net present worth.

Appendix Table 5

Projects	Irrigation		Power		Best combination or single project
Single purpose	Dam	−10	Hydro	6	14
	Tube wells	−18	Thermal	14	
Multipurpose					13

In this case it is the best single purpose project which is to be compared to the multipurpose one, and if it is of higher net present worth, preferred. If no combination or project has at least zero net present worth, none qualifies as an economically desirable project.

12. Sometimes it is unnecessary to elaborate the costs and benefits of all four separate single purpose projects and of the multipurpose project. First the net present value of the multipurpose project must be evaluated. Next, values of the independent single purpose projects (thermal power and tube wells) are determined, and if they are negative, rejected. Finally, it is necessary to evaluate one of the single purpose projects, hydroelectric power or dam irrigation, which make up the multipurpose project. If one has a positive net present worth higher than the alternative in its sector (power or irrigation),[4] it is not necessary to evaluate separately the other. Appendix Table 6 illustrates this point. For the present, figures in parentheses should be ignored.

---

[4] Or if the alternative does not exist, simply has a positive net present worth.

66

Appendix Table 6

Projects	Irrigation		Power		Best combination or single project
Single purpose	Dam	16 (10)	Hydro	? }	23 or
	Tube wells	10 (16)	Thermal	7 }	?
Multipurpose					21

13. In the example above, the net present worth of the hydroelectric project has not been assessed separately, but that of dam irrigation is known, and also of the multipurpose project of which both form a part.[5] Both are positive. Net present worths of thermal power and of tube well irrigation are also known, and are positive. Since the dam is preferred to the tube wells, the only two combinations of single projects to be considered are:

i) Dam plus hydro
ii) Dam plus thermal

The first of these is always inferior to the multipurpose project. Therefore the only comparison necessary is between:

ii) Dam plus thermal
iii) Multipurpose

The dam plus thermal combination is better.

14. If the figures in parentheses apply, and the tube wells are preferable to the dam, this argument cannot be used, because the initial comparison will be as follows and there is insufficient information:

i) Tube wells plus hydro (unknown)
ii) Tube wells plus thermal (23)

---

[5] It is thus possible to calculate by subtraction the net present worth of the additional investment required to obtain the hydroelectric benefits of the multipurpose project. Here, however, it is only necessary to note that this will always be greater than the net present worth of the hydroelectric project separately, since costs are shared.

The only restraint on the value of the net present worth of hydro is that it must be less than 11, because the net present worth of the multipurpose project (21) is greater than that of dam (10) plus hydro separately. If the net present worth of hydro is greater than 7, combination (i) will be better than (ii). No choice can therefore be made between (i) and (ii) without evaluation of the separate hydro project.

15.   Below, in Appendix Table 7, the reverse case is shown (again ignoring the figures in parentheses) where the net present worth of dam irrigation is unknown but where that of the separate hydro-electric project is known, is positive or zero, and is better than that of thermal power. In these conditions, the best choice apparent is also the only comparison with the multipurpose project necessary.

Appendix Table 7

Projects	Irrigation		Power	Best combination or single project
Single purpose	Dam	?	Hydro 13 (7) ⎫	23 or
	Tube wells	10	Thermal 7 (13) ⎭	?
Multipurpose				21

Again, in the case in parentheses in the above table, where the known element of the multipurpose project is *not* superior in its sector as a separate project, it will be necessary to evaluate the unknown element separately. For although the net present worth of the dam irrigation must be less than 14, it might be greater than 10, and then dam irrigation and thermal power would be the best choice.

16.   There is a second condition. Not only must the known element be superior in its sector as a separate project, but it must also have a non-negative net present worth. Otherwise, although the multi-purpose project has necessarily a greater net present worth than the combination of dam and hydro as single projects, the unknown component by itself might have a still higher net present worth.

To illustrate, let us assume that in Appendix Table 5 above, the net present worth of hydro, taken separately, is unknown (but is in fact 16). Following the previous argument, the thermal alternative alone then appears as the best of the known choices, although the hydro alternative alone would in fact be better still.

IV.
EVALUATION WITHOUT SPECIFIC VALUE FOR POWER

17. So far, specific economic values have been assumed for the benefits of power, whether from hydro or thermal plants. Normally, however, as discussed in the main paper, the problem is set up in such a way that the same volume of power is to be produced by either project. The levels of gross benefits are unspecified, but are the same for both power investments. The comparison of the hydro and thermal projects is thus reduced to a cost comparison rather than a comparison of both costs and benefits. This causes some further complications for the evaluation of multipurpose projects, as illustrated in the following example:

Appendix Table 8

Project	Investment costs (discounted)	Benefits (discounted)	Net present worth
Dam irrigation	100	113	13
Hydro power	100	$e-13$	$e-113$
Multipurpose	150	$e+100$	$e-50$
Tube well irrigation	50	68	18
Thermal power	40	$e-54$	$e-94$

Here e stands for the discounted gross value of the power produced, and is the same for the thermal and the hydro project. 13 represents discounted current costs of hydro plant, and 54 those of thermal plant, so that $e - 13$ and $e - 54$ indicate the discounted net benefits from hydro power and from thermal power, respectively. The value of e is not further specified, but is related to the economic value of power to the economy.

18.   To a large extent, the fact that the benefits of power are not given any specific value does not upset the method of calculation. The comparisons may be set out as before:

Appendix Table 9

Projects	Irrigation		Power		Best combination or single project
Single purpose	Dam	13	Hydro	e−113	e−76,
	Tube well	18	Thermal	e− 94	or 18 if e< 94
Multipurpose					e−50

The multipurpose project is the best choice of the alternatives which include power. Tube wells are the best single purpose irrigation project. The multipurpose project has a higher net present worth only if e − 50> 18. If e< 68, tube well irrigation by itself is the best choice. Thus the final selection depends on the value of e.

19.   The general conclusion is that the value attributed to the power benefits may determine whether the multipurpose project should be carried out. It is possible without evaluating the benefits from power to determine the best project among the single-purpose power projects, the combinations of irrigation and power projects and the multipurpose project, for in these comparisons, e drops out. But since the benefits are only then expressed in some such form as e − 50, it is uncertain whether they are positive and, more specifically, greater than the benefits from the better single-purpose irrigation project. However, to determine this, it will not always be necessary to estimate the value of e precisely, but only to say whether it is sensibly above or below the relevant figure—in this case 68.

20.   The problem is similar, of course, to that in the simple hydro/thermal comparisons discussed in the main paper. One can say negatively, for instance, that a hydro project is "out," but not, positively, that the thermal project is "in," without giving a value to the power benefits at least equal to their minimum costs. This valuation is implied in the basic assumption underlying this type of analysis, that the expected demand for power *must* be met.